JAMES TAYLOR

THE BIG 3 MUSIC CORPORATION/NEW YORK

Editor: HERBERT WISE
Design: IRA FRIEDLANDER
Piano: LEO ALFASSY
Guitar: HAPPY TRAUM

JAMES TAYLOR

CONTENTS

PHOTOGRAPHS:
Norman Seeff, covers, 6, 10
Marie Cosindas, 4, 8
Katherine Tweed, 9
Peter Asher, 12, 13, 16
David Gahr, 14, 17, 20
Herbert Wise, 18
Gary Legon, 19
Globe Photos (John Hamilton)
    22, 25, 28, 29b, 31, 33
The Family Album, 15

JAMES TAYLOR

TWA In-Flight (Indeed)
Dear Pete and Judy,
I thought to make things easier for you perhaps. The stewardess was kind enough to bring paper and pencil and Peter (Asher) has given me an envelope; so I will write about myself (as always). I am flying to Martha's Vineyard which is what I call home and I should be there tomorrow morning if this jet doesn't crash.

Word has it I was born at 5:06 P.M. (approx.) on March 12, 1948, at Boston's General Hospital where Isaac, my father, was studying medicine. My mother, Gertrude, bore four children—Alexander, myself, Kate and Livingston — in that town, and one more, Hugh, in the town of Chapel Hill, N.C., where my father later joined the staff of the University of North Carolina Medical School. Today he is the dean of that school.

My siblings, like me, show an interest in music and some will find a living there. We grew up and went to school in Chapel Hill—a nice place to grow up—and now we are scattered along the east coast. I love my family.

As far back as I can clearly remember my family summered on Martha's Vineyard Island. Once we went to Maine and when I was ten my mother took us all to Europe.

At the age of fourteen I returned to Milton, Mass., where Isaac and Trudy lived at the time of my birth. I went to a private boys boarding school in that town for more or less five years. It seemed to please my parents. There's not much to say here. I had some friends but I was often sad. ➤➤

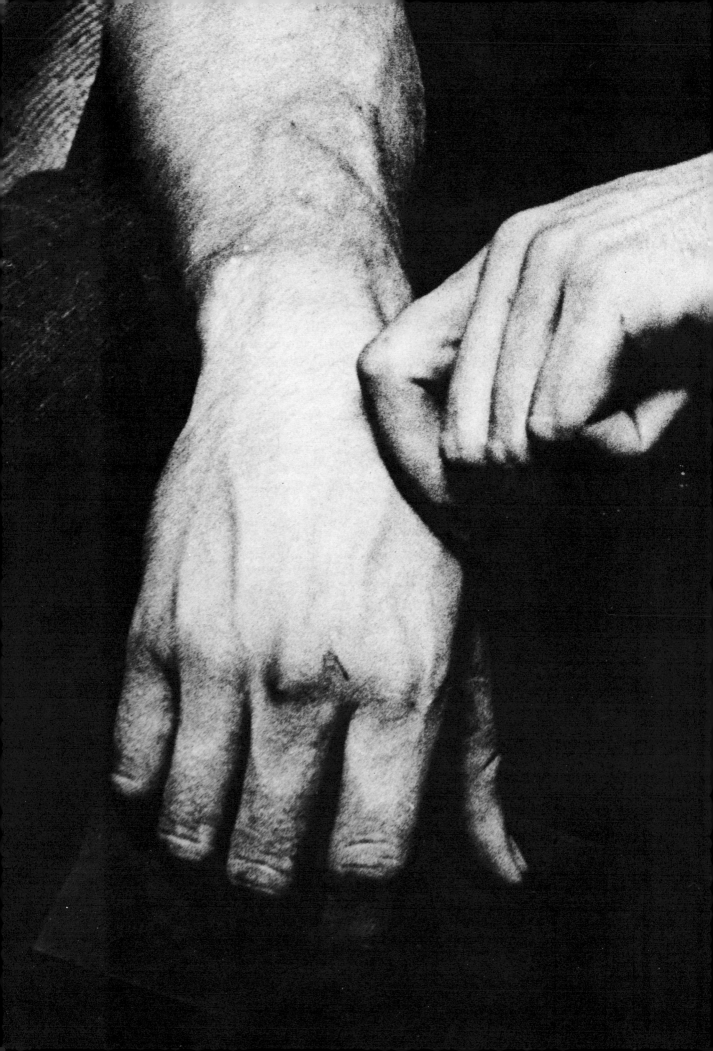

Much later, in the summer of 1965, I lost my virginity and went to Russia. So much for that summer—how exciting.

In the fall of 1965 I entered a state of what must have been intense adolescence—"These are the best years of your lives"—and spent nine months of voluntary commitment at McLean Psychiatric Hospital in Massachusetts.

I split that place and in the summer of '66 left for New York to form a musical group with three friends: the Flying Machine. Danny (Kootch) Kortchmar—guitar; Zach Wiesner (and later Jerry Burnham)—bass; Joel Bishop O'Brien—drums; and James (Stringbean) Taylor—guitar. We were a good band. I wrote a lot. I became involved with some heavy drugs. New York was hard on me and after a year I left and the Flying Machine disbanded.

As far as music is concerned it simply seems to have happened. When I was younger I played the cello and took some theoretic music in school; but formal studies never agreed with me and, for whatever reason, I took up the guitar on my own. People like to talk generally about roots, but I find it difficult. I am the product of a haphazard musical environment which, I suppose, makes me a folk artist. Green rock 'n' roll. Words about my lyrics are at best redundant.

Peter and I met in London. I had intended to travel but I ended up recording for Apple. Peter and I work well together. Now we are with Warner Brothers, but I owe my first album to the Beatles.

I have 27 acres of land on Martha's Vineyard Island where I hope to build a home, and I seem to be set for life. We all seem to be set for life.

Love,
James

"I'm getting more and more into performing. I used to think of myself just as a writer, but I still feel as though I'm a writer who's being asked to sing songs. That's okay; that's good. It's a nice slant."

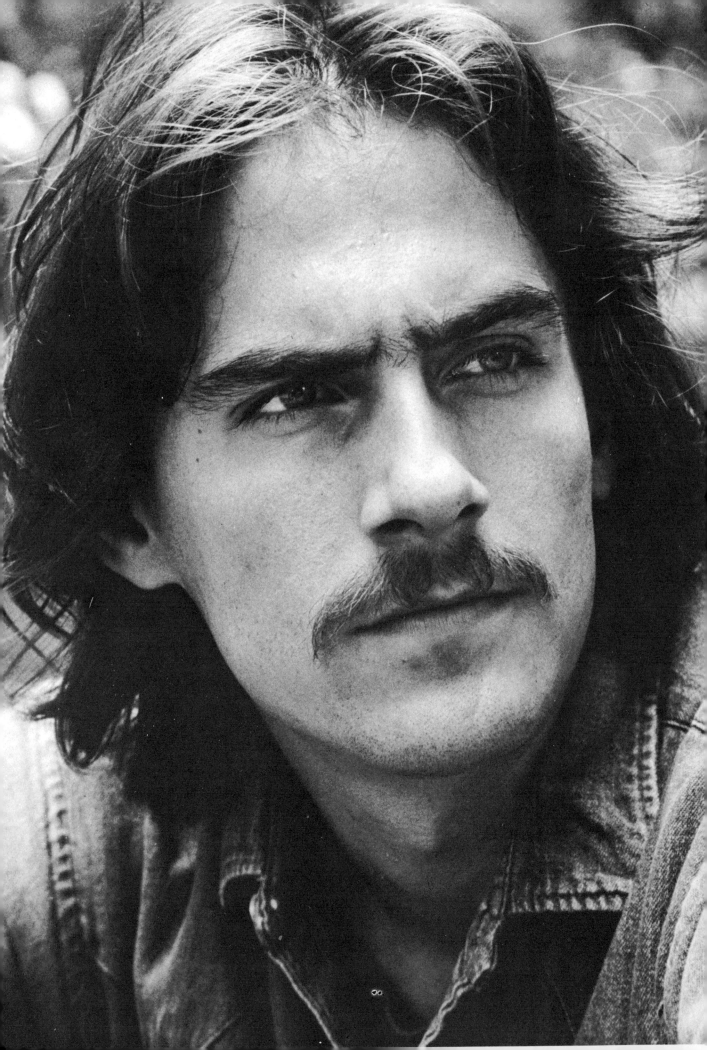

"I remember when I was about ten years old or so there was a guy who played guitar for us. Gee, I thought that was great and I wanted to play his guitar. His name was Damon Coe—perhaps his name was Geoffrey Coe."

Dr. Taylor and James

The Corsairs

From Apple

James Taylor has the distinction of being the first artist signed to the Apple stable who is not a horse; a man with the patience of a saint, for he was one of the last to be released, who is not in prison. It took ninety days to construct this long playing record and it will take considerably fewer days to be recognized as a testimony to his musical heritage.

James Taylor was born twenty summers ago to the state of Massachusetts in the city of Boston of Dr. and Mrs. Vernon Taylor. For companionship he received a sister Kate and brother Livingston. The good Dr. Taylor moved his young wife and children to the rain forests of Chapel Hill, North Carolina; it was in Chapel Hill that James Taylor grew tall in the shadows of a verdant and awesome land.

He was eighteen when he arrived in the city so big they had to name it twice; New York, New York. (If you are British, you won't understand). He lost himself in music on the lower East Side with a contingent musically labelled The Flying Machine.

An obscure young man, explaining himself and his attitudes only sparingly, he arrived in the London Summer of '68 with a piece of paper that carried the name "Peter Asher". The previous day Peter had received the post of Chief of A & R for Apple Records. Two hours later he signed the contract and a little more than three months after he had completed twelve tracks on black wax produced by Peter, and it is an album that will bring him out of the shadows and into the light. It is one great song and will be sung, strummed and enjoyed through the auspices of Zapcor, world famous for service with a smile. Glad to have you with us James, and "get well soon" say Apple over the Atlantic for James is nowadays not well in New York, New York.

Apple Corps Ltd 3 Savile Row London W1 Telephone 01-734 8232 Telex Apcore London

Peter Asher

CARNEGIE HALL

Gary Legon Reprinted from Rock Magazine by permission of the publisher

James Taylor is a very humble person; so humble in fact, that at rehearsals for his concert, if Peter Asher hadn't been there to see to it that things got done, nothing would have. James would have been the last person to insist that anybody do anything.

The rehearsal scene was generally a gas. The rhythm section used on the last album was flown in from L.A., with the beautiful Carole King playing piano, Kootch (Danny Kortchmar) on guitar, Russ Kunkel on drums, Lee Sklar on bass, and a horn section made up of some of New York's finest and assorted musician friends and helpers.

We walked the 10 or 15 blocks (yep, walked) from the rehearsal hall to the hotel. A fan came up and walked along with us for a couple of blocks, and James went along with the whole thing. He congratulated James on the Warner Bros. album, and you could see James really meant the thanks he gave him.

James' debut show at Carnegie Hall was two beautiful hours of James Taylor. He started by himself, doing "With A Little Help From My Friends." He did a mixture with Joni Mitchell's "For Free" and Carole King's "Up On The Roof." James did a song by his younger brother Livingston, and threw in a JT Coke commercial. The first half ended with James being joined by Kootch on acoustic guitar for "Lo and Behold," "Baby Don't Loose Your Lip On Me," and "Night Owl Blues," dedicated to their (the Flying Machine's) old days, and a Kootch song about "Machine Gun Kelly."

The second half opened with James alone doing "Circle Round The Sun," "Carolina," "Something In The Way She Moves," and "Brighten Your Night With My Day," Carole King then joined him on piano for "Blossom," and they were joined by the rhythm section for "Country Road," "Taking It In" and Anywhere Like Heaven." The only down of the entire show was a mediocre version of an already overheard song, "Let It Be."

James told us about the time a friend and he wrote a song in the nuthouse. "I was in there for... a little while... that was the diagnosis at the time. We'd go into the bushes and smoke some herbs and then we'd go back to the padded rooms and wait for the man to come by and peep in. While doing "Knocking Round The Zoo," the horn section came on and really hit it; they stayed out, and with the band all together now they went into "The Blues Is Just A Bad Dream," "Don't Talk Now," "Steamroller" and "Suite For 20 G."

The show ended with an encore of "Sweet Baby James," and the audience glided out into the night, six inches off the ground.

"No, writing doesn't come very easy. It doesn't come very often. And I don't know why that is. The central idea musically and lyrically comes out at the same time, and then I just work around that. That's what usually happens."

SWEET BABY JAMES

Alfred Aronowitz

Those people spilling off the curb into MacDougal St. last Saturday noon weren't there to watch the eclipse. Not until May 1, 2079, will New York be able to see the moon darken the sun again, but those people standing in MacDougal St. have come to witness an event of obviously greater magnitude. James Taylor was making his only appearance of the year at the Gaslight, and they were waiting to buy tickets.

Who is James Taylor, this young, thin giant with long, dark hair and a wispy beard who walks through the crowds that come to adore him with a half-smile on his lips and distant visions in his eyes like a Jesus in an era when we already have too many, and at the same time one too few? Ask him about himself and he will give you only the barest outlines of a life that was lived for the most part in hurt. You don't talk to Sweet Baby James. You listen to his music.

He tells about himself in the slow, measured phrasing of someone who doesn't want to be misunderstood. His voice is clear crystal. Whatever secrets James Taylor has about himself, he thinks his music is big enough to hide behind. James Taylor steps upon the stage ready to challenge the gods.

Four years ago, he was one of those kid musicians among the hundreds of groups hustling through the Village for any ear that would listen to their own particular cries of prophecy in the wilderness. He belonged to the Flying Machine, a band which is now, as he sings, with sweet dreams in pieces of the ground. When the Flying Machine crashed, so did James.

A couple of years later, he turned up in London and recorded an album for Peter Asher of Apple Records. The album was distributed in this country by Capitol but as Peter says, "I got the feeling Capitol never listened to it." His new album, "Sweet Baby James," is on Warner Brothers and, only a few weeks after its release, James is drawing the kind of crowds you saw standing on the street outside the Gaslight. On Saturday night alone, the club had to turn away 2,000 people, "I can feel it happening," James says. "I'm starting to feel good about it."

The songs that James sings are his own, born out of the torture that twice sent him into mental institutions. His lyrics are, of course, private, personal and mysterious, but at 21, James speaks for his generation with the kind of cool authority that seems destined to elect him one of the spokesmen of his time. Could he be the one, born in Boston and raised in Chapel Hill, the son of the dean of the University of North Carolina Medical School?

He was 17 and in boarding school the first time he committed himself. "I was suicidal," he says. "It was the only place I could go." He committed himself a second time after recording his first album. "It seemed like a good idea at the time," he explains.

You watch him singing on the stage of the Gaslight, sounding exactly as he sounds on his album, and you feel his confidence surrounding you. It's already a little too close in the room and you wonder if you like being crowded by his presence. Sweat from a water pipe collects on the ceiling and begins to drip on him. "My guitar is gently weeping," he says. He sings a Coke commercial and everyone laughs.

"Lord knows you got to take time to think these days," he says. Before he begins to sing again, he tells the audience, "If you feel like singing along, don't." Is James Taylor going to be the next public phenomenon? It's a little early in the cycle for such an event, but that's the league James has applied for. May the Lord have mercy on him.

TWO LANE BLACKTOP

Jacoba Atlas

DURANT, Oklahoma—James Taylor is in Oklahoma on the sixth week of filming his first movie. The strain of motion picture acting is taking its toll; the interminable waits, the plodding slowness, have all left James rather on edge. Still enthusiastic about the overall outcome of the film, but doubting his future as an actor, James expressed his biggest complaint: "Sitting around waiting."

In the film, Two-Lane Blacktop, James portrays the driver of a 1955 Chevrolet dragster. Two-Lane is being shot entirely in location, in such "large" cities as Tucumcari, New Mexico, Boswell, Oklahoma and Little Rock, Arkansas. The director is Monte Hellman.

I have met James a few times at the home of his manager, friend and producer, Peter Asher. James is infinitely easy to talk to—and impossible to interview. He is a private man, not given to philosophical interpretations of either his work or his actions. He likes to talk about "things" but refuses to delve deeply into the stuff of which interviews are supposedly made.

We had lunch together on location in what looked like a burnt out school auditorium. James, half joking, said: "Now you're going to bleed me."

James had signed to do the film without reading the script—in fact, he explained that Hellman had kept the script from the actors well into shooting. "We'd get the dialogue in the morning and just learn the one day. He finally let us see a dialogue script. But Peter (Asher) had read it and liked it, and I met with Monte and thought he was a good dude. Rudi too." Rudi is Rudi Wurlitzer, the screenwriter of Two-Lane Blacktop.

James had spent the entire morning, after rising for a 6 am call, walking across the only main street in Boswell, Oklahoma. By 12:30 the company broke for a 30-minute lunch and James explained that he'd be doing variations on that walk all afternoon. "I don't have any lines, today," he said somewhat reluctantly.

Lunch proved better in expectation than in reality. The food was far from appetizing. Finally breaking, James disgustedly said under his breath "They expect me to work all afternoon after eating this?" It was the only time James truly complained.

He spent most of the breaks during the day singing bits and pieces of songs, his own and other people's. When co-actor Warren Oates, said, noting the load of food on the only actress in the picture's plate: "Pack it in," James launched into a chorus of Joni Mitchell's "Song About The Midway," singing "pack it in/I heard you did/pack in, in in . . ."

He did concede that working on this film has provided better nutrition than he's had in months. "I can't cook at all, and I don't have a wife." Suggestions of obtaining either a wife or a cook were left unanswered.

He has become tired of people likening Two-Lane Blacktop to Easy Rider, simply because both films deal with seemingly free travel across the United States. "They're very different," he explained to a local writer for what must have been the hundredth time. "Our film has characters totally without egos. Not like Easy Rider.

James is anxious to get back to

his home in Martha's Vineyard (an island off the coast of Mass.); he is helping to build his own house and is worried that it won't be completed before winter sets in. "I'll only have about two weeks at home, between this picture and concert commitments and the house has to be made ready to support me through the winter. I worked on it a lot before the film, got me in shape."

James' first gig when completing Two-Lane Blacktop will be at the Troubador (L.A.) in November, sharing the bill with his friend, Carol King. The last time James played that club, Carol had worked in his band, now she will solo. "I guess we'll play together, though. Each sitting in on the other's set. Her album's great."

James is somewhat anxious to take a year off from performing and settle into his house and write. He has written only intermittently while filming and is worried that contractual commitments will keep him from Martha's Vineyard for long periods.

"We're going to start recording another album, very shortly, I have some new material all ready. We taped one of my concerts at Carnegie Hall and I wanted to do a special pressing of it, about 80 or 100 copies, to give as Christmas presents to my friends, but Peter said it would be bootlegged immediately. But I wouldn't care about that."

His recording of "Fire and Rain" has finally been released by Warner Bros. as a single, James says, "as an afterthought. They released 'Sweet Baby James' first, but nobody played it and nobody bought it." He recently played on a Joni Mitchell session for a single called "California" but that too has not yet been released.

Joni and James had been up in Canada together playing a benefit, but there are no future plans for a combined album or concert work. Cryptically he explained the reluctance for a joint venture: "You have to be careful what you take money for."

He has not really met a great deal of hostility on the road because of his long-haired "hippie" appearance, but in some towns there have been cat-calls and cries of "come here, girlie.' James has refused to respond.

The seemingly long shooting schedule (actually the eight weeks allotted for the film is brutally short) has resulted in all night singing and playing sessions for the crew and other members of the cast, and a generally good attitude prevails. The crew of the film has taken to James, accepting his friendly inaccessibility.

But whatever attitude prevails, nothing compensates for the waiting. "I don't have any control," James said forcefully. "I don't like not being in control." An actor is, of course, the person with the least amount of control working on any film.

When I left to go back to Los Angeles people looked at me as if we were all in prison and I was the only one with a reprieve. We joked about even Los Angeles looking good. Two days later, James and cast and crew of Two Lane Blacktops were in their cars and buses travelling the few hundred miles to the next location, Little Rock, Arkansas. From there on to Memphis, Tennessee and the end of shooting.

From Melody Maker, reprinted by permission

Dennis Wilson

Monte Hellman

Warren Oates

TWO LANE BLACKTOP

Laurie Bird   Dennis Wilson

A REFUGEE FROM ACADEMIA BLUDGEONS TO DEATH A POET

Susan Donaghue

Recently, we ventured to Bryn Mawr, Pa., to interview James Taylor at The Main Point where he was playing to capacity crowds. The interview took place between James' first and second sets, and so is, necessarily, a short (but pithy) one. Despite his apology that he was 'a bit off tonight,' he struggled fiercely to be Polonius for his inquisitor, who insisted that he was Hamlet, and not just an attendant lord. The 300-watt blue eyes that 'have seen fire and rain' have seen a lot more, but prefer to let the songs tell it.

Would you start and give us some sort of biographical stuff first?

I was born in Boston and my family moved to North Carolina and right now I live on Martha's Vineyard island in Massachusetts. I was just in a motorcycle accident last summer and I broke both my hands.

Was *Carolina In My Mind* more than just a daydream then? Since you did live there?

Well, I won't go into it too much, because it is a mistake to try and explain songs, but it is a frame of mind, really. It just describes a feeling. It's just a song, I guess, about homesickness, or about wanting to come home.

That was one question I wanted to ask you: why all your songs are about sunshine or going home? It seems the more I listen to the albums the more I hear either one of those two themes. Either sunshine or going home.

Well, that's not necessarily true. They are not *all* that way. There are some love songs in there and there are other, different kinds of things, too.

You know you have been academicized, so to speak . . . A lot of contemporary poetry classes now use your material, I understand. What do you think of your lyrics being distributed out to 40 members of a poetry class?

Well, I don't know. You see, I just write the songs. I don't have to analyze them. I think of myself as being a romantic, pretty much. Whatever that really means.

In the traditional sense?

Yeah. I am not very studied in it. But, I don't have to be.

Can you really talk about songs, though? Can you break them down?

No, I don't like to talk about my songs. I think it is a mistake for me to talk about songs. It is self-defeating, it is the antithesis of what a songwriter wants to do. He writes a song so that he doesn't have to talk about it.

Do you think that we are murderers to dissect them?

Oh, no, no.

You don't care then whether other people do, you just prefer not to yourself?

Well, you see, a song either affects someone or it doesn't affect them. There is no choice, you know. The listener doesn't have any choice as to whether he *likes* the song or *doesn't* like it. He can't take exceptions to a song, or at least to one of my songs.

It either hits him or else it doesn't. I mean either it connects or it doesn't connect. And that is what is nice about it. You come out and say something direct and categorical and definitive, then someone can take exception to it, and say yes or no. But if someone hears a song and it happens to really reach him, it is more direct.

Can you separate the two when you say "reach him"? That seems to imply that art has to necessarily have some sort of emotional connection . . . which your songs do, of course. Is this what you're after?

I don't have any real objective. It is hard to say. I think that all good art is kinetic art, but I don't think it necessarily should move externally. I think that my songs move people, or I like to think that they move people, inwardly, back in towards

themselves, introspectively. Instead of moving them actively or externally.

Primarily, I don't have any objectives that I might talk about, purely after the fact. I write the songs because it is the only thing I know how to do, and I write the songs because I have to, and I would write songs even if I wasn't a songwriter. I know that sounds paradoxical, but it is true.

Writing the songs because you have to: if you've got it in you then it has got to come out?

Well, it doesn't have to. My own personal opinion is that I don't have too much choice in the matter.

I don't know whether it is necessity or not. I have to make a living. And, aside from that, I'm an American and a product of the 20th century environment and I have *got* to do something, you know. It may not mean anything, but that is what I do.

Where does that leave the idea of talent?

Whether or not I, or anyone else, have talent is up to other people. Whether or not my songs are good or my singing is good, that is for someone else to judge. I don't make that judgment myself. I think they're good. But I would think they are good even if other people thought they were terrible.

What I noticed in your album and what I noticed in the set that I heard upstairs, is that you seem to be a man who has faith. Your songs are filled with faith or at least pointing out the necessity of some kind of faith. I think talent becomes something very secondary to that, something that fits into the context of faith. It seems like a personal kind of thing between you and the audience upstairs. I was watching your eyes and watching how you communicate with these people, and I couldn't get the word faith out of my mind.

Yeah...I know, you know. But is it good ...that's good then.

You seem almost deprecatory about the things you have done.

They are the only things I do. It is hard for me to explain, but, you see, I'm not a talker. Not to...don't get me wrong...not to exercise false modesty, but...

I didn't have the feeling that you were doing that at all.

That is what I offer. That is what my work is. The songs are what my work is. And talking about them and talking about myself and analysis or elaboration or whatever, isn't what I do, because in itself it is enough. That is all that I need to do.

Almost the only thing that I can give other people is songs, and the rest of it is mine, just my private life, my private mundane life. There isn't anything special about me, living day to day, just doing what I do.

Then where do the songs come from?
I don't know. They come from everywhere and they come through me. The songs that I write, at any rate. They come from everywhere and they come through me. Until they stop coming through me. They also come through a lot of other people.

Who influenced you as a songwriter?
It is hard to say. I don't know who has influenced me as a songwriter. I haven't studied or consciously emulated anyone, as far as I know.

How about readings? This may seem a silly question, but do you think of yourself primarily as a lyricist or as a musician, what comes first? Your songs or your music?
I don't know. I suppose it is about the same. One growing out of the other, and I guess they come together. I find it difficult to write lyrics unless I write my music at the same time.

I would like to write. I have tried to. I have entertained the idea of writing a book or something like that, short stories, you know. But I don't find myself too able to do that.

Why not?
I don't know. It is just not one of the things I do yet.

Can you write songs both when you are happy and when you are down?
Different songs come out of different moods.

I write a lot when I am doing something else that occupies my time but not necessarily all of my mind. I write some songs when I'm driving a car or chopping wood, something like that.

I can't sit down and write a song like the good professional song writer can. I wish I could. I can't just sit down and say well, I'll designate a couple of hours and sit down and write a song. Oh, I have done it before, but that is not usually what happens. They just come to me, or through me or whatever.

Then were you goofing upstairs when you asked the people to buy your record to make you rich...
Well, it *is* a joke. It is said to get a laugh, but I always also want people to listen to it. You know, I would be lying if I said that I didn't want people to buy my records.

Do you think that you have something that you're telling people, something that is important for them to listen to?
I think that I am telling some people things—well, I don't know, it depends on the person. If they find it important, then it *is*. If they find it entertaining or enjoyable, or if it makes them feel good, or if it makes them feel more, then that is good too.

Are you trying to make anybody change?
No, I'm not trying to make anybody change.

Suggest **a change to anyone?**
Maybe that, I don't know?

All these answers that end with "I don't know" almost suggest someone who is possessed, the way you said, "I do it because I have to do it." Someone who is almost possessed by his art. Do you feel that way?
Well, I would except that that I don't take it that seriously. I don't take *any*thing that seriously. It is easy for me. Easy.

Why don't you look at people?
What do you mean?

You don't look at people when you sing, and you are not looking now...
I can't see.

You can't see? Onstage?
No, it's dark out there.

Well you are not looking at people now either.
I don't know why not. Maybe it embarrasses me.

Would you like to do...
Different things. I'm a pretty central character. I want to build a house, I want to eventually have some animals and children. I don't consider that there is any great cause or anything that I could lend myself to, any objective. I just want to do what the next person wants to do and that is to continue living. The end...there is no end, just living.

Casting yourself into the existential void?
Sure, why not, man, I don't know. I think that kind of analysis maybe is born of discomfort and I feel pretty comfortable.

Reprinted from Jazz and Pop,
by permission of the publisher

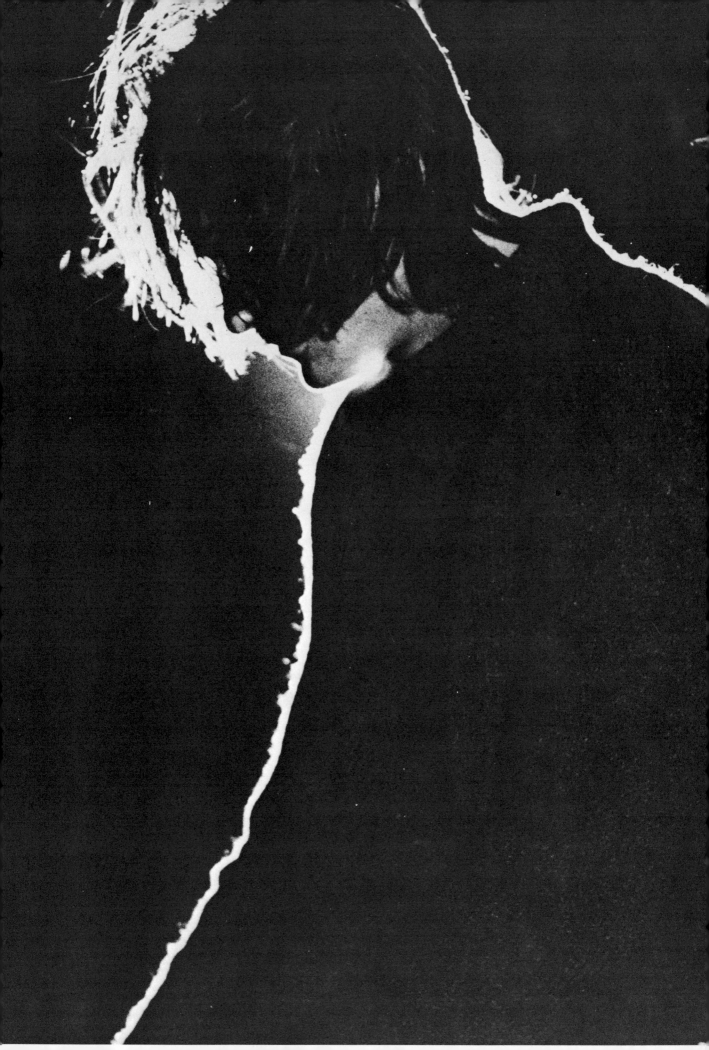

Fire and Rain

James Taylor

Sunny Skies

James Taylor

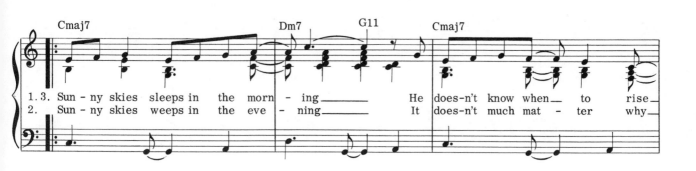

1.3. Sun - ny skies sleeps in the morn - ing_____ He does-n't know when_ to rise
2. Sun - ny skies weeps in the eve - ning_____ It does-n't much mat - ter why

He clos - es his wear - y eyes_ up - on_ the day
I guess he just has_ to cry_ from time_ to time_

Look at him yawn - ing   Throw-ing his morn-
Ev - 'ry-one's leav - ing   And sun - ny skies has_

- in' hours_ a - way_
— to stay_ be - hind_ He knows how to ease down slow.

Ev-'ry-thing is fine in the end_ And you will be pleased to know That

sun - ny skies has - n't a friend._

And throws it all_ a - way_

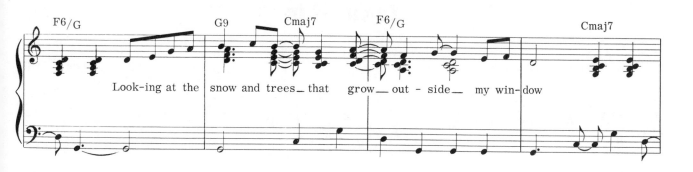

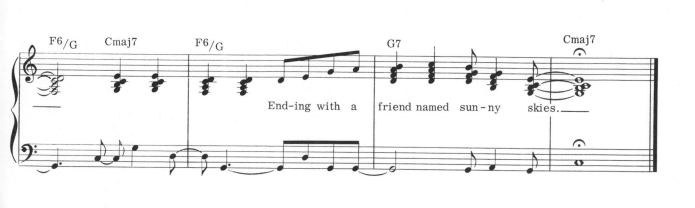

Takin' It In

James Taylor

Something In The Way She Moves

James Taylor

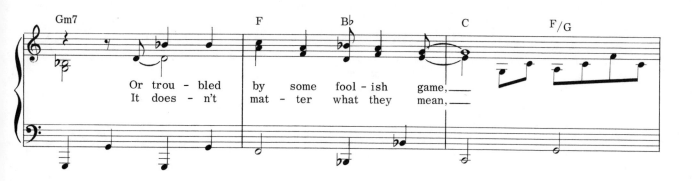

Or trou - bled by some fool - ish game,___
It does - n't mat - ter what they mean,___

She al - ways seems to make me change___ my mind.
She says them most - ly just to calm___ me down.

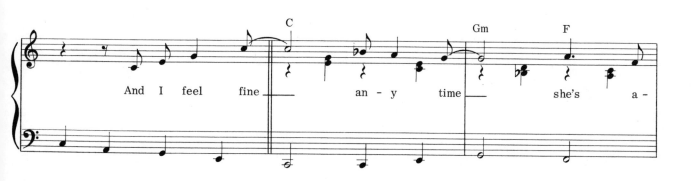

And I feel fine___ an - y time___ she's a -

round me now,_____ She's a - round me now,___

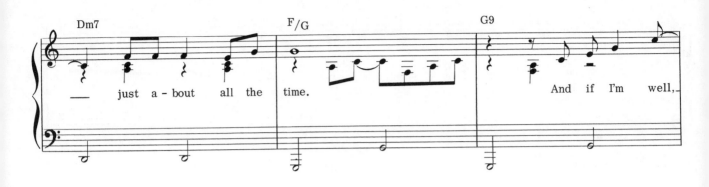

just a-bout all the time. And if I'm well,

you can tell ___ she's been with me now, ___ she's been

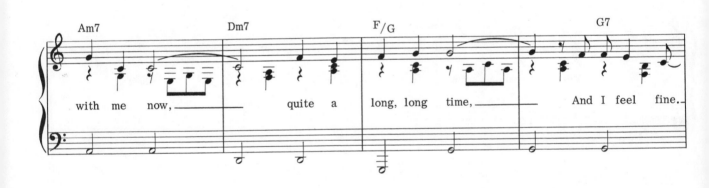

with me now, ___ quite a long, long time, ___ And I feel fine.

Brighten Your Night With My Day

James Taylor

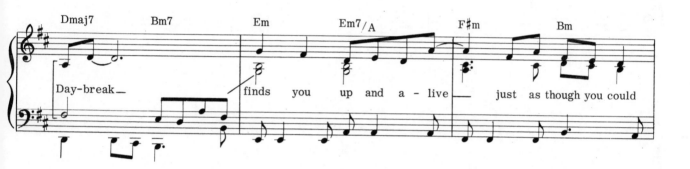

Day-break— finds you up and a-live— just as though you could

touch a star;— But sun-set— seems to leave you wear-y a-

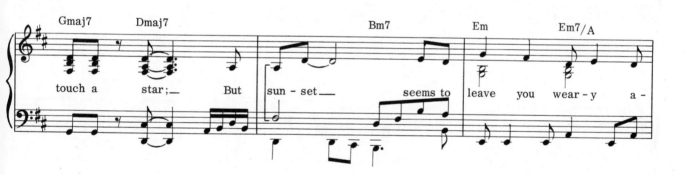

lone— and won-der-ing who you are.— Don't de-ny that lone-

Country Road

James Taylor

Ma-ma don't un - der-stand— it — she wants to know where I've been. I'd

have to be some— kind of nat-ural born fool to want to pass that way a - gain— But you know I could
(2nd time) But I could be

feel it—
there, Lord.—
On a coun-try road—

Sail on— home to Je - sus won't you good girls— and boys?—

I'm all— in piec - es you can have your own— choice— But

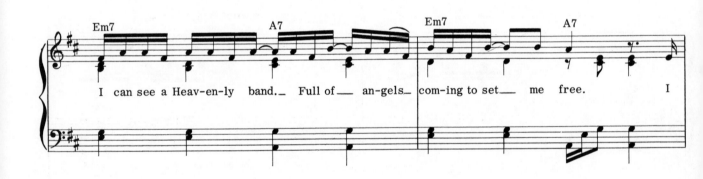

I can see a Heav-en-ly band.— Full of— an-gels— com-ing to set— me free. I

don't know noth-ing 'bout the why or when, but I can tell you that it's bound to be— be-cause I could

Sweet Baby James

James Taylor

Don't Talk Now

James Taylor

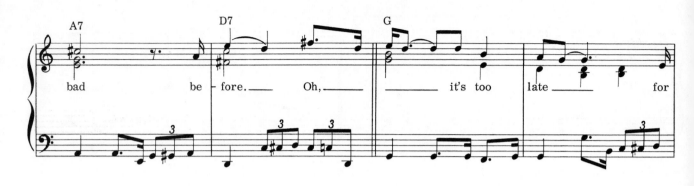

bad be - fore. ___ Oh, ___ ___ it's too late _____ for

me to lie, And I can't make a

sec - ond try. _____ I just came home back, babe, got to

say good - bye, ___ good - bye. Don't talk now.

Sunshine, Sunshine

James Taylor

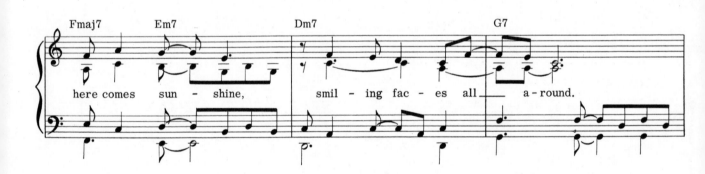

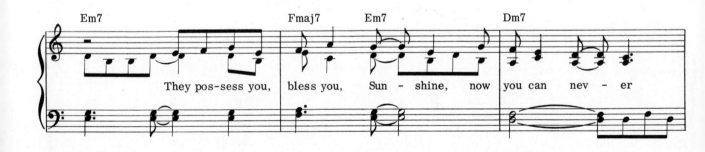

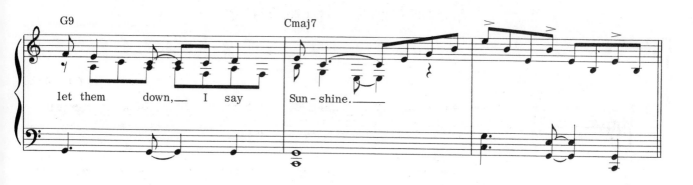

let them down,_ I say Sun - shine._

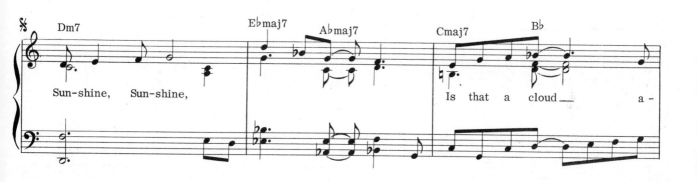

Sun-shine, Sun-shine, Is that a cloud _ a -

cross your smile, _ or did you dream ___ a - gain last night? _

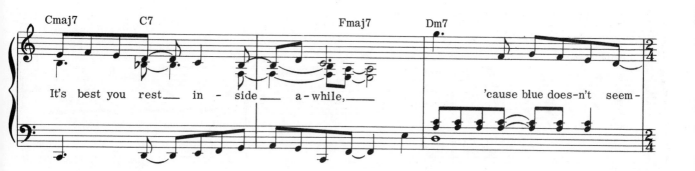

It's best you rest _ in - side _ a - while, _ 'cause blue does-n't seem -

2. Rising too late to chase the cold,
   failing to change the frost-bitten dew,
She's trading her mood of yellow gold,
   for frost-bitten shades of silver blue.
Friends and lovers, past and gone,
   and no one waiting further on;
I'm running short of things to be,
   and sunshine means a lot to me.
Sunshine, oh, sunshine.

Oh Baby Don't Loose Your Lip On Me

James Taylor

Anywhere Like Heaven

James Taylor

Something's Wrong

James Taylor

74

Steam Roller

Slow blues

James Taylor

Well, I'm a steam-roll-er, babe, — I'm bound to roll all o-ver you.

Yes, I'm a steam-roll-er, now, — babe, I'm bound to roll — all o-ver you.

Well, I'm a dem-o-li-tion der - by, ___ yea!___ A heft-y hunk of steam-ing junk.

Now, I'm a na-palm bomb, babe, Just guar-an-teed to blow your mind.

Yea, I'm a

na-palm bomb___ for you, ba - by, ___ Whoa ___ guar-an-teed, just ___

guar-an-teed ___ to blow your mind, yea. ___

If I can't have your love for my own ___ now, ___ sweet child, Won't be noth-ing left be-hind ___

It seems like late-ly, babe, ___ got a bad case of steam-roll-er blues. ___

Blossom

James Taylor

G **F** **C6/E** **D7sus** **C** **C/B** **Am7** **D7sus**

Blos-som smile—some sun-shine down—my way— Late-ly I've—been lone-some
Blos-som there's—an emp-ty road—be-hind— Sit you down—be-side—me

G **F** **C6/E** **D7sus** **C** **C/B** **Am7** **D7sus**

Blos-som it's—been much—too long—a day— It seems my dreams—have fro-zen
Blos-som there's—a sweet—dream on—my mind— There's a song—in-side—me

B♭maj7 **Am7** **D7sus G** **C** **D Em7 D7 C** **Bm7 C Bm7 Em7**

Melt my cares—a-way. Send the sun-shine down—my way—when-ev-
Take these chains—a-way.

The Blues Is Just A Bad Dream

James Taylor

3. My mind is rambling
   It's just like some rolling stone
   Since that nightmares come to stay
   My thoughts just don't belong
   They say the blues is just a bad dream
   They say it lives inside your head
   But when it's lonely in the morning
   You're bound to wish that you were dead.

Rainy Day Man

James Taylor

ask a - gain!_ Go on and pray for rain!_ It looks like an - oth - er fall,_

_ your friends they don't seem to help at all._ Now, when you're

feel-ing kind of cold and small_ just look up your rain - y day man_

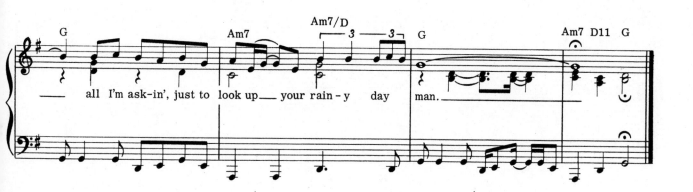

_ all I'm ask-in', just to look up_ your rain - y day man._

Knocking 'Round The Zoo

James Taylor

count-ing all the spoons, babe. And if I'm feel - ing edg-

- y, there's a chick who's paid___ to be my slave,

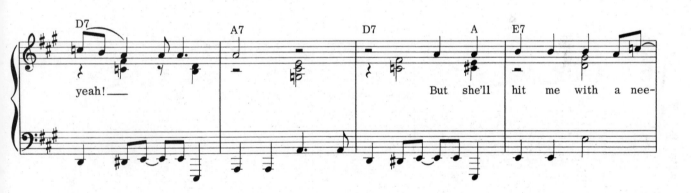

yeah!___ But she'll hit me with a nee-

- dle if she thinks I'm try - ing to mis - be - have.___

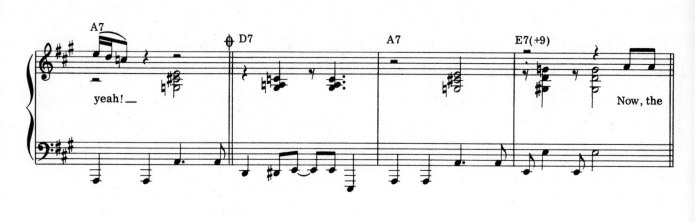

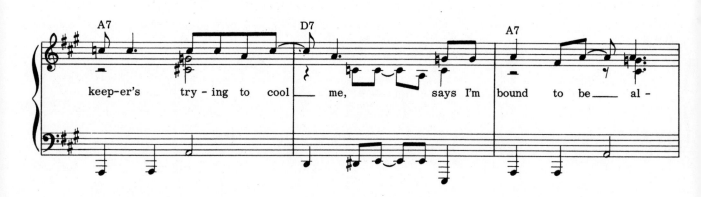

-y ev-'ry time I make a sud-den move

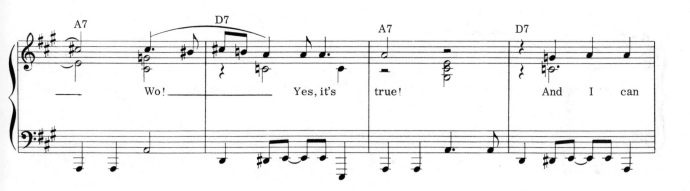

Wo! Yes, it's true! And I can

hear him cel - e - brat - ing ev - 'ry time I up and leave the room.

Now, my

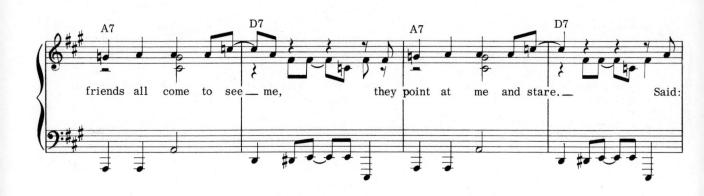

friends all come to see — me, they point at me and stare. — Said:

"He's just like the rest — of us, — so what's he do-ing in there?" — They

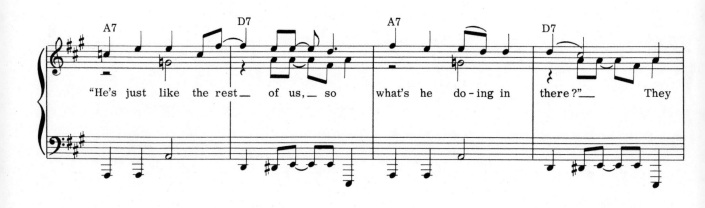

hide in their mov - ie the-a-tres drink-ing juice, keep-ing

tight. 'Cause they're

cer - tain 'bout one thing, babe, that zoo's no place to spend the night, oh,

no! Just

Repeat and fade

Lo and Behold

James Taylor

Some shall sink___ and___ some shall rise.___

Ev-'ry-one's talk-ing 'bout the train to glo - ry___

Long, long time till it gets___ here to you ba - by.___ There's a

well _____ on the hill, Let it be.___

Night Owl

Moderate 4

James Taylor

—— and run-ning 'till they're too tired—— for hav-ing fun,—— But when the

sun goes down—— and then bright —— lights shine—— my day-time has just be-gun,——

—— Woh, I'm a night owl, hon - ey, woh—— sleep all —— day——

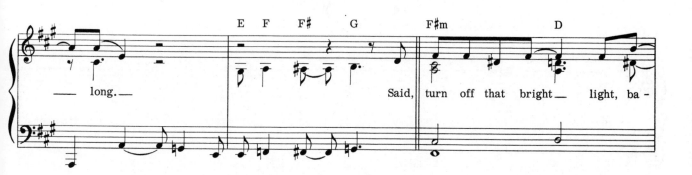

—— long.—— Said, turn off that bright —— light, ba -

Repeat and fade

Suite for 20G

James Taylor

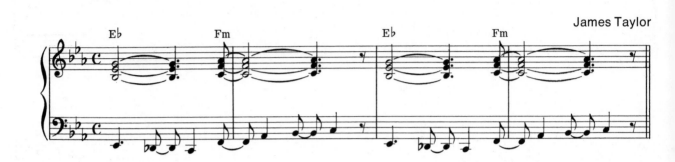

Slip-ping a - way__ what can__ I say__ Won't you stay__ in - side__ my month__

__ of May__ And hold on to__ me gold - en day,__ slip-ping a - way.

Sun - shine__ on__ my wall to

I've been try - ing hard __ to find a - way __ to let __ you know __
This time 'round I'm search - ing down __ to where __ I used __ to go __

That we can make __ it shine __ most all __ the time.
And it's been on __ my mind __ to make __ it shine.

You can say, __ "I want __ to be __ free."

Carolina In My Mind

James Taylor

Moderate 2

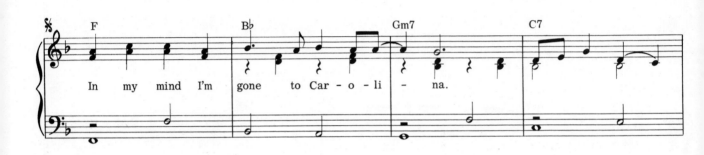

In my mind I'm gone to Car-o-li-na.

Can't you see the sun-shine? And can't you just feel the moon-shine?___ And

ain't it just like a friend of mine___ to hit me from___ be-hind?___ And I'm

gone to Car - o - li - na in my mind.

Kar - in she's a sil-ver sun, you'd best walk her a-way and watch it shine.
Dark and si - lent late last night, I think I might have heard the high-way call.

Watch her watch the morn-ing come.
Geese in flight and dogs that bite. And

sil-ver tear ap - pear-ing now I'm cry - ing ain't I? I'm
signs that might be o - mens say I'm go - ing, go - ing, I'm

gone to Car - o - li - na in my mind. There

110

GUITAR

THE GUITAR OF JAMES TAYLOR

Happy Traum

James Taylor's guitar style, like his singing, is subtle, easy-going and so distinctive as to be almost a trade-mark. He is a fine guitarist who sticks to simple, easily recognizable riffs, often repeating the same ones from song to song. His chord progressions and musical concepts, though, are deceptively complex as you will find as you get into these transcriptions and try to make it come out sounding like James Taylor. Making something complex *sound* simple is the mark of a fine artist, and James does it, even in the tone quality he gets out of his guitar.

Most of James' songs are played in a three-finger picking style (he does not use picks when he plays) and the intros, runs and breaks have been transcribed are in that style: the thumb plays the bass (6th, 5th, and 4th) strings, and the index and middle fingers play the high strings. I have transcribed what I considered to be the most important and useful (to the student) guitar parts in the arrangements on James' records. Using these as an aid, you will be able to reconstruct the whole arrangement and use it in a way that suits *your* style best. Anytime a guitar line or chord pattern stands out so that a student would say, "now how does he get that sound," I have tried to capture it on paper. In many cases, once it is learned, it can be used similarly in other songs. At other times, the sound can be achieved by simply playing the chords in the proper inversions, and so I have diagrammed them accordingly.

The tablature used is the one that is becoming more or less standard in folk music and other guitar instruction books. Six lines, each represent a string on the guitar, with a number on a string representing the fret at which the string is depressed. Thus, means that you press the second string at the first fret, making a C note. The C chord would be written like this:

SUNSHINE SUNSHINE

Sounds of laughter here comes sunshine smiling faces all around
They posess you bless you sunshine now you can never let them down
        I say Sunshine

Sunshine Sunshine,
  Is that a cloud across your smile - or did you dream again last night
  It's best you rest inside a while - as blue doesn't seem to suit you right

Things ain't what they used to be - pain and rain and misery
Illness in the family and Sunshine means a lot to me
        I say Sunshine
But could it be Sunshine is drifting with midnight,
And lonely when everyone's gone
Blue crystal spirits and gardens in moonlight
Leave her weak - alone and bleak - all quiet and grey by dawn

Sunshine Sunshine,
Rising too late to chase the cold and failing to change the frost to dew
She's trading her mood of yellow gold for frost-bitten shades of silver-blue

Friends and lovers past and gone and no-one waiting further on
I'm running short of things to be and Sunshine means a lot to me
       I say Sunshine ..... Sunshine

© 1968, 1970 Blackwood Music, Inc./Country Road Music, Inc.

BRIGHTEN YOUR NIGHT WITH MY DAY

Daybreak finds you up and alive - just as though you could touch a star
But sunset seems to leave you weary-alone and wondering who you are
Don't deny that lonely feeling that keeps stealing on you from deep down inside
Hey can't you see that it's no good concealing a feeling it hurts you to hide

when you can come home to me -
    yes I'm happy to hear what you've got to say to me baby - all the way
Girl you can count on me -
    watch those shadows fade away - and brighten your night with my day

Daybreak sunset hot and cold   running smiles and tears
a bright outside to match your foolish pride but not a word for the lonely years

Please come back home to me -
    now you won't have to say that you'll stay with me baby - it's not that way
Just come back home to me -
    throw that worried look away - and brighten your night with my day

© 1967, 1970 Blackwood Music, Inc./Country Road Music, Inc.

THE BLUES IS JUST A BAD DREAM

A tree grows in my back-yard It only grows at night
It's branches they're all twisted And it's leaves are afraid of light

CHORUS
They say the blues is just a bad dream
    They say it lives inside your head
But when it's lonely in the morning
    You're bound to wish that you were dead

There's winds out on the ocean They're blowing where they choose
But them winds ain't got no emotion And they don't know the blues
     (CHORUS)

My mind is rambling rambling It's just like some rolling stone
Since that nightmare's come to stay My thoughts just don't belong
     (CHORUS)

© 1969, 1970 Blackwood Music, Inc./Country Road Music, Inc.

SOMETHING'S WRONG

Something's wrong, that restless feeling's been preying on your mind
Road maps in a well-cracked ceiling - the signs aren't hard to find
Now I'm not saying that you've been mistreated
No-one's hurt you - nothing's wrong
A moment's rest was all you needed
So pack your things and kindly move along

Like dust in the wind you're gone forever

You're wind-blown leaves you're a change in the weather

Just a town like any other a second brand-new start
A third or fourth-hand wife or lover no, you won't break her heart
Take some bacon - ▓▓▓▓ go on and leave your watch-chain
She won't count on nothing more
Wrap your hands around that small-change
And tip-toe bearfoot out the door

Yes something's wrong that restless feeling's been preying on ~~my~~ mind
When things get bad I'm bound to pack my bags and just
Leave them all behind

DON'T TALK NOW

Where I've been - you don't know
What I've got - it don't show
Now I won't try - to teach you how
Don't talk now

Don't talk roads - don't talk sand
Don't talk dust - don't talk (no) man
Don't talk rules - don't talk vows

Don't talk now

I don't want to hear the same old song
And too many rights still make her wrong
She can't hurt me less by talking more
She can't make good what was bad before

It's too late - for me to lie
And I can't make - a second try
I just came back - to say good-bye
                    (good-bye)
Don't talk now

Nah Nah Neh Nah - Nah Neh Nah Nah
Nah Neh Neh Nah - Nah Neh Nah Nah
Nah Nah ~~Nah~~ Neh Nah - Nah Neh Nah Nah
Nah Neh Nah Nah - Don't talk now

CAROLINA IN MY MIND

CHORUS
In my mind I'm gone to Carolina
Can't you see the sunshine.
Can't you just feel the moonshine
And ain't it just like a friend of mine
            to hit me from behind
And I'm gone to Carolina in my mind

Karin she's a silver sun
        you'd best walk her way and watch it shine
Watch her watch the morning come
A silver tear appearing now I'm crying ain't I
        gone to Carolina in my mind
There ain't no doubt in no-one's mind
        that love's the finest thing around
Whisper something soft and kind
And hey babe the sky's on fire I'm dying ain't I
        gone to Carolina in my mind
(CHORUS)

Dark and silent late last night
        'think I might have heard the highway call
Geese in flight and dogs that bight
And signs that might be omens say I'm going going
        gone to Carolina in my mind

Now with a holy host of others standing 'round me
Still I'm on the dark side of the moon
And it seems like it goes on like this forever
        you must forgive me

(CHORUS)
(CHORUS)

KNOCKING 'ROUND THE ZOO

Just knocking around the zoo on a Thursday afternoon
There's bars on all the windows and they're counting up the spoons
And if I'm feeling edgy there's a chick who's paid to be my slave
But she'll hit me with a needle if she thinks I'm trying to misbehave

Now the keeper's trying to cool me says I'm bound to be alright
But I know that he can't fool me 'cause I'm putting him uptight
And I can feel him getting edgy every time I make a sudden move
And I can hear him celebrating every time I up and leave the room

Now my friends all come to see me they point at me and stare
Said he's just like the rest of us so what's he doing in there
They hide in their movie theaters drinking juice - keeping tight
Cause they're certain about one thing that zoo's no place to spend the night

Just knocking around the zoo on a Thursday afternoon
There's bars on all the windows and they're counting up the spoons
And if I'm feeling edgy there's a chick who's paid to be my slave
But she'll hit me with a needle if she thinks I'm trying to misbehave

NIGHT OWL

A catfish he tends to groove on the water it's just where he's bound to be And a monkey kind of flashes on fruits and bananas so he lives in the top of a tree But my eyes are made for darkness and so the night-time is right for me Said I'm a night-owl, honey - sleep all day long Now most folks they like the good day time baby they like to see the shining sun They're up in the morning off and running 'till they're too tired for having fun But when the sun goes down and them bright lights shine my day time has just begun Woh I'm a night owl, honey woh sleep all day long Said turn off that bright light baby you're just about to drive me blind Draw them curtains for me mama you watch and you'll see how my love light shines Now there's two sides to this great big world and one of them is always night Hey if you can take care of business in the sunshine baby I guess you're going to be alright But don't come looking for string-bean to lend you hand because my eyes they just can't stand the light No I'm a night-owt, honey-sleep all sleep all day long I said sleep all day long Woh I'm a night-owl, honey said I'm a night-owl honey yeh yeah said I'm a night-owl honey jump on the night train coming on by your door I said yeh yeh yeah woh ho yeah night owl baby you gotta try just a taste said wait and see you're gonna be fine with me said I'm a night-owl baby ho gotta hey yeah said I'm a night-owl honey yeh yeah Woh I'm a night-owl honey I'm a nightowl woooooh I'm a night-owl baby yeh yeah I said wooooo yeah woh no-o I'm a night-owl baby yeh yeah.

SOMETHING IN THE WAY SHE MOVES

There's something in the way she moves
Or looks my way or calls my name
That seems to leave this troubled world behind
And if I'm feeling down and blue
Or troubled by some foolish game
She always seems to make me change my mind

And I feel fine anytime she's around me now
She's around me now almost all the time
And if I'm well you can tell she's been with me now
She's been with me now quite a long long time
And I feel fine

Every now and then the things I lean on lose their meaning
And I find myself careening
Into places where I shouldn't let me go
She has the power to go where no-one else can find me
And to silently remind me
Of the happiness and good-times that I know

It is n't what she's got to say
Or how she thinks or where she's been
To me the words are nice the way they sound
I like to hear them best that way
It doesn't matter what they mean
She says them mostly just to calm me down

And I feel fine anytime she's around me now
She's around me now almost all the time
And if I'm well you can tell she's been with me now
She's been with me now quite a long long time
And I feel fine

TAKING IT IN

Morning - sing me a song
Afternoon - bring it along
Night.time - show me a friend
      say it again
      send a good dream my way
Wednesday - feeling just fine
Got to say time on my hands
Friday - look at them run
      show me some fun
      taking the sunshine in

God knows you've got to give yourself time to think these days
Lord knows you've got to take enough time to look both ways

The pieces fly by so quickly now

Laura - look at you walk
I swear you've got eyes in my head
I'd like to - follow you down
      show you around
      borrow the crown you wear
Bacon - lie on that plate
Blackeyed peas wait on the side
'Gravy - chicken and rice
      isn't it nice
      tell me the price of food
What happens when the answers they give you aren't good enough
What happens when it rains for eight days on your week off
You know you can't buy tomorrow - no

It's all a matter of opening up your eyes and looking around
'Cause it's all there' - it's all there

I said taking the sunshine in

RAINY DAY MAN

What good is that happy lie
All you wanted from the start was to cry
It looks like another fall
Your friends don't seem to help at all
Now when you've feeling kind of cold and small
Just look up your rainy day man

It does you no good to pretend
You've made a hole much too big to mend
And it looks like you lose again my friend
So go on home and look up your rainy day man

Now rainy day man don't like sunshine
Don't chase no rainbows he don't need good-times
Grey days rolling then you'll see him
I said empty feeling now you need him

All those noble thoughts don't belong
You can't hide the truth with a happy song
And since you knew where you stood all along
Just call on your rainy day man

Simple pleasures all evade you
Store - bought treasures none can save you
Look for signs to ease the pain
Ask again - prey for rain

It looks like another fall
Your friends don't seem to help at all
Now when you're feeling kind of cold and small
Just look up your rainy day man - all I'm asking
      just to look up your rainy day man

CIRCLE ROUND THE SUN (TRADITIONAL)

I love my baby
      And she's bound to love me some
Yes I love my baby
      And she's bound to love me some
She throws her arms around me
      Like a circle around the sun

I lay down last night
      Just trying to take my rest
I lay down last night
      I was trying to take my rest
But my thoughts they just kept wandering
      Like the wild geese in the west

Now I know that sunrise
      Is going to shine in my back-yard some day
Yes I know that sunrise
      It's bound to shine in my back-yard some day
And the wind it will rise up
      And blow my blues away

I love my baby
      And she's bound to love me some
Yes I love my baby
      And she's bound to love me some
She throws her arms around me
      Like a circle 'round the sun

FIRE AND RAIN

Just yesterday morning they let me know you were gone
Susan the plans they made put an end to you
I walked out this morning and I wrote down this song
I just can't remember who to send it to

    I've seen fire and I've seen rain
    I've seen sunny days that I thought would never end
    I've seen lonely times when I could not find a friend
    But I always thought I'd see you again

Won't you look down upon me Jesus you've got to help me make a stand
You've just got to see me through another day
My body's aching and my time is at hand
And I won't make it any other way

Now I'm walking my mind to an easy time
                my back turned towards the sun
Lord knows when the cold wind blows
                it'll turn your head around
There's hours of time on the telephone line
                to talk about things to come
Sweet dreams and flying machines in pieces on the ground

BLOSSOM

Blossom smile some sunshine down my way
Lately I've been lonesome
Blossom it's been much to long aday
It seems my dreams have frozen
Melt my cares away

Send the sunshine down my way
    whenever you call my name
I know what you mean to say
    to me it's all the same

Blossom there's an empty road behind
Sit you down beside me
Blossom there's a sweet dream on my mind
There's a song inside me
Take these chains away

OH BABY DON'T YOU LOOSE YOUR LIP ON ME

Oh baby don't you loose your lip on me
Oh baby don't you loose your lip on me
I've tried so hard to be your good boy
Tell me what more can I be

ANYWHERE LIKE HEAVEN

When I walk along your city streets
   and look into your eyes
When I see that simple sadness
   that upon your features lies
If my spirit starts to sink
   it comes as no surprise
It's been a long way from anywhere
   like heaven - to your town

There's a pasture in the countryside
   I used to call my own
There's a natural pillow for my head
   the grass there is overgrown
I think of that place from time to time
   when I want to be alone
It's been a long way from anywhere
   like heaven to this town

People live from day to day
   but they do not count the time
They don't see their days
   slipping by - and neither do I

SUITE FOR 20G

Slipping away What can I say
Won't you stay inside me month of May
And hold on to me golden day, slipping away

Sunshine on my wall
   to keep my mind on the things I'm saying
Footsteps in the hall
   to tell me I've been this way before · nevermore

Let it rain sweet Mary-Jane
Let it wash your love down all around me
Come inside and put it down · let it rain

I've been trying hard to find a way to let you know
That we can make it shine most all the time
This time 'round I'm searching down to where I used to go
And it's been on my mind to make it shine

You can say I want to be free
I can say some day I will be

When I catch a common cold
I want to hear a saxophone
When I let the good times roll
Slide me a bass trombone
Walk me down old Funky Street
Lord knows I feel good enough to eat
Hold my soul · I sure am fond of my rock 'n roll
When I go to sleep at night
I want to hear a slide guitar
when I'm feeling loose and right
Riding in my automobile
Boney Maroney and Peggy Sue
Rocking pneumonia and boogey-woogey flue
Hold my soul · I'm sure enough fond of my rock 'n roll
Good God

SWEET BABY JAMES

There is a young cowboy He lives on the range
His horse and his cattle are his only companions
He works in the saddle and he sleeps in the canyons
Waiting for summer, his pastures to change

And as the moon rises he sits by his fire
Thinking about women and glasses of beer
And closing his eyes as the doggies retire
He sings out a song which is soft but it's clear
As if maybe someone could hear

He says

CHORUS
Goodnight you moon light ladies
Rockabye sweet baby James
Deep greens and blues are the colors I choose
Won't you let me go down in my dreams
And rockabye sweet baby James

The first of December was covered with snow
So was the turnpike from Stockbridge to Boston
The Berkshires seemed dream-like on account of that frosting
With ten miles behind me and ten thousand more to go

There's a song that they sing when they take to the highway
A song that they sing when the take to the sea
A song that they sing of their home in the sky
Maybe you can believe it if it helps you to sleep
But singing works just fine for me

© 1970 Blackwood Music, Inc./Country Road Music, Inc.

SUNNY SKIES

Sunny Skies sleeps in the morning
He doesn't know when to rise
He closes his weary eyes upon the day
              look at him yawning
Throwing his morning hours away

He knows how to ease down slow
Everything is fine in the end
And you will be pleased to know
That Sunny Skies hasn't a friend

Sunny Skies weeps in the evening
It doesn't much matter why
I guess he just has to cry from time to time
Every ones leaving
And Sunny Skies has to stay behind

Sunny Skies sleeps in the morning
He doesn't know when to rise
He closes his weary eyes upon the day
 And throws it all away

Looking at the snow and trees that grow
              out-side my window
Looking at the things that pass me by
Wondering if where I've been is worth
              the things I've been through
Ending with a friend named Sunny Skies

© 1969, 1970 Blackwood Music, Inc./Country Road Music, Inc.

LO AND BEHOLD

Lonely by day - Empty and cold
Only to say - lo and behold
Deep in the night - down in my dreams
Glorious sight - this soul has seen

There's a well on the hill
You just can't krill for Jesus
There's a well on the hill
Let it be
I don't build no heathen temples
where the Lord has laid his hand
There's a well on the hill
Let it be

Everyone's talking 'bout the gospel story
Some shall sink and some shall rise
Everyone's talking 'bout the train to glory
Long time 'til it gets to you baby

© 1970 Blackwood Music, Inc./Country Road Music, Inc.

STEAM-ROLLER

I'm a steam roller baby
I'm going to roll all over you
I'm going to inject your soul
with sweet rock 'n roll
And shoot you full of rhythm and blues

I'm a cement mixer
A churning urn of burning funk
I'm a demolition derby
A hefty hunk of steaming junk

I'm a napalm bomb
Guaranteed to blow your mind
And if I can't have your love
Won't be nothing left behind

© 1970 Blackwood Music, Inc./Country Road Music, Inc.

COUNTRY ROAD

Take to the highway won't you lend me your name
Your way and my way seem to be one and the same

Mamma don't understand it
She wants to know where I've been
I'd have to be some kind of natural-born fool
to want to pass that way again
But I could feel it - on a country road

Sail on home to Jesus won't you good girls and boys
I'm all in pieces - You can have your own choice

But I can hear a heavenly band full of angels
Coming to set me free
I don't know nothing 'bout the why or when
But I can tell you that it's bound to be
Because I could feel it - on a country road

I guess my feet know where they want me to go
Walking on a country road
Walk on down

© 1970 Blackwood Music, Inc./Country Road Music, Inc.